Date Due

Too many Cooks.....

BY WILLIAM WIESNER

J. B. Lippincott Company

PHILADELPHIA   NEW YORK

verything

has a beginning.

When the cat is away
the mice will play.

on't put all your eggs
in one basket.

Where there is smoke
there is fire.

ook before you leap.

oo many cooks
spoil the broth.

Birds of a feather

flock together.

ever put off till tomorrow

what you can do today.

bird in the hand is worth
two in the bush.

A poor workman
    blames his tools.

essels large may venture more,

but little boats should keep near shore.

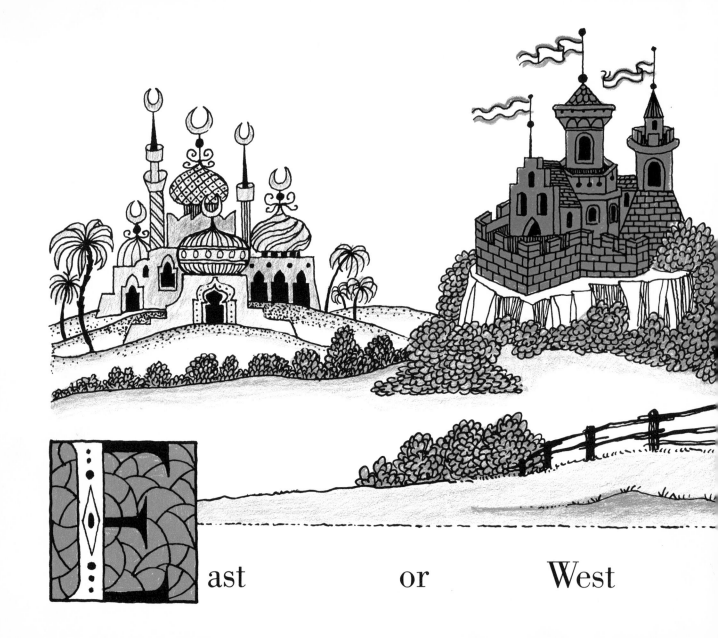

East   or   West

home   is   best.

aste makes waste.

t is better to be safe
than sorry.

All's Well That Ends Well